Be a Jane or Jill...Don't Be A Dick

For more please visit us online at www.DontBeADickBook.com

Dedication

To Kylie, Bryan, Andrew and Drake for allowing your Dad to chase his dreams. To Jenny who has stuck with me through a lot of craziness. And for all those who are out there trying to make the world a better place. A special thanks to Arody Victoria who never says "no" when I need a hand— true friend and amazing illustrator. Last special shout out to those who are fearless in their lives and have influenced mine- you all know who you are— thank you.
- Thomas

As always thank you God, my great assistants Neyda, Ariana and Giancarlo and to all my family... Hey Tom one more project for the road, thanks brother!
- Arody

Follow us on: **f** bejanenotdick

ISBN: 978-0-9973954-0-2
First Edition. March., 2016

BE A JANE OR JILL... DON'T BE A DICK

By

Thomas Morgan

Illustrated by

Arody J. Victoria

Dick, Jane and Jill were friends.

They all graduated at the same time from a great school _____

All received respected degrees and had promising careers ahead of them.

They were very well liked and had visions of financial success beyond their wildest dreams. *They seemed unstoppable.*

One day, on the way home from work, Jane saw

the most horrible injustice.

It was beyond anything she had thought possible. It was heartbreaking, horrifying, devastating, cruel...

and it was right there in front of them.

What Jane didn't realize is that this horrible injustice had in fact been right there, on the same corner, every day they had gone home.

But today for some reason she
saw it and now, because of Jane,
they all saw it.

Jane decided, on that day, there was more she must do. This was bigger than money. This was important enough to sacrifice everything for. She must stop this!

The next day Jane quit her job. She ran down to that corner

and used all of her skill, all of her education, all of her problem

solving and heart and started her mission to stop the injustice

— by making everyone see it — acknowledge it
— and become part of the solution to fix it

Jill too was a vital part of a solution—but in a different capacity—finding ways to use her corporate voice to help Jane and to provide assistance.

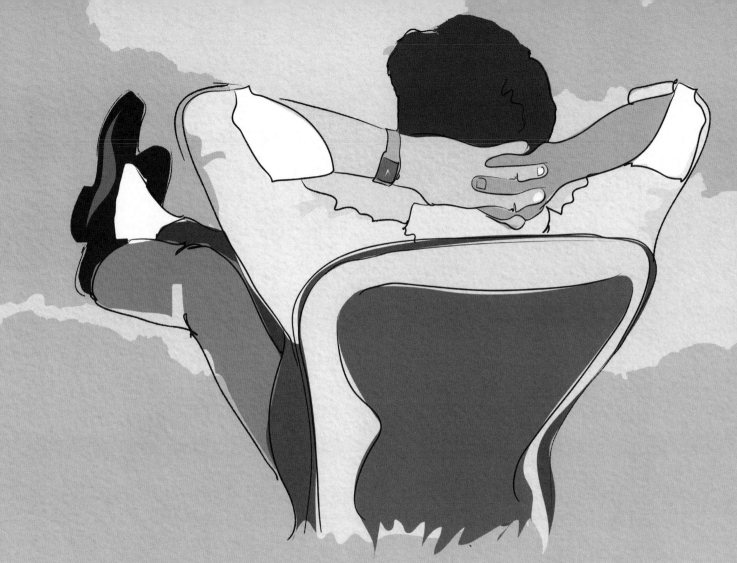

Dick did nothing. Instead he would sit in his office and look down on that corner and laugh at Jane. He pointed her out to others saying how ridiculous she was for trying such a thing. Surely she would fail.

Dick thought those Jane was trying to help were, in fact, deserving of the way they were treated. If they had been smart and hardworking like him they wouldn't be in this position.

Years later they all came back for their college reunion.

Jill spoke of her fantastic career as her innovative ways of combining philanthropy with her company's brand. It had not only helped provide a great deal of funding to Jane and her causes but, remarkably, had increased sales. This giving and new way of thinking had in fact made her company one of the most desirable in the world to work for—as there was a greater good beyond just the widget they produced. Her compassion had also served her well as a leader and all who worked with her had true admiration of her commitment to company and the community.

Jane went on to be the global voice and was credited for stopping the injustice she had first seen on that corner. She was well respected as a compassionate innovator and would go on to do the same for many causes and injustices around the world. She spoke to huge audiences around the world-lending all of her knowledge, passion and grit to take on and solve issues that many saw as unsolvable.

Dick was rich. He spoke only of his possessions — his cars, his money... his fancy house, expensive vacations and how he had front row tickets to the best games. He didn't have much involvement in his community and could not speak to much beyond his work.

His life an legacy would be defined by his corner office and nameplate.

Each of you have a chance to be a Jane

a Jill or a Dick.

Don't be a Dick.

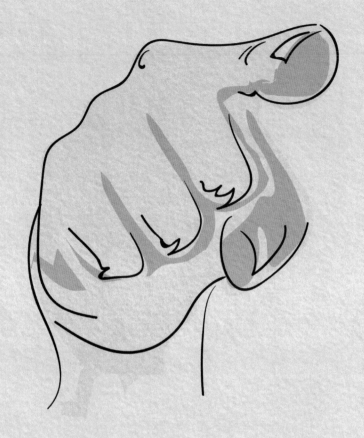

Money is important to sustain yourself but it is not who you are. You have a chance to be amazing and by amazing I mean world changing, through being compassionate in your companies, in your communities and on that corner that needs you most right now.

Be a Jane, or a Jill. Be part of a change not only by being involved yourselves but also supporting those corporations who do the right thing, who are engaged in their communities, who give back.

You will make mistakes. You will take the wrong path. You will end up somewhere you will wish you hadn't (many of you may have already experienced this).

These moments of Dick-dum don't have to define the rest of your life.

You can change—you can be a Jane or a Jill. It's not too late!

Also know that there are a lot of Dicks out there – and they wont change by telling them this story or by telling them they're a Dick. They will change when they see good examples, when they see success and happiness that comes from a Jill or a Jane and when they are given the opportunity to take part in something bigger. I would encourage all of you to continue to invite your Dicks to the corner—no matter how many times he says "No"...

Congratulations!

Now, get involved and please

Don't be a Dick.

Made in the USA
Lexington, KY
17 March 2016